"IT'S O.K. TO SAY NO TO ... of helping parents to teach ... se is unhealthy and unwise, as well as specific ... ng peer pressure to use drugs. I strongly feel that it should reach all parents with young children."

—Bill Beacham, Director of Educational Services
IMPACT Training

"This is a sensible and sensitive book, designed to foster parent-child cooperation, resulting in a child's knowing how to say No to alcohol and other drugs."

—Deerfield Citizens for Drug Awareness

"Just as you teach your child to stay away from fire and to look both ways before crossing the street, you need to teach your child to say No! to drug use. IT'S O.K. TO SAY NO TO DRUGS! can be a vital step in this process. This book will help your child develop the attitude which will make future involvement less likely. And, most important, it will teach your child specific resistance techniques that work. IT'S O.K. TO SAY NO TO DRUGS! is a powerful preventive tool. Teach your child to say No! to drugs, and you are really teaching you child to say Yes! to health and life."

—Dr. Manuel Selya
Clinical psychologist specializing
in drug abuse

TO THE CHILD

"My philosophy has always been—and my advice to you—is to learn as much as you can about the particular subject you are trying to make a decision about. So when it comes time to make that decision, you will know what is right and what is wrong. And you will make the correct decision yourself. You will do it because you know it is right, or won't do it because you know it is wrong. Without any pressure from anyone.

"It's O.K. to say No to anything, especially when you know it's wrong."

— Dave Jennings
New York Jets

TO THE PARENT

"The approach (to drug use) adopted by IT'S O.K. TO SAY NO TO DRUGS! is a direct one: the only response to an offer of drugs is to simply refuse. The child and parent are provided with a multitude of 'high-risk situations' for initiation of drug use. In each case the mandated response is identical—to say No."

— Dr. Alan Marlatt, Director
Addictive Behaviors Research Center
University of Washington

"Without being frightening, IT'S O.K. TO SAY NO TO DRUGS! teaches children that the only possible response to drug use is to say No."

— National Kid Watch Program
1–800–KID WATCH

IT'S O.K. TO SAY NO TO DRUGS!

A PARENT/CHILD MANUAL FOR THE PROTECTION OF CHILDREN

ALAN GARNER

Illustrated by Rick Detorie

TOR

A TOM DOHERTY ASSOCIATES BOOK

Look for these other books in the *It's O.K.* series:

IT'S O.K. TO SAY NO!
SOMETIMES IT'S O.K. TO TELL SECRETS!

Acknowledgments

To Dr. Doris Lee McCoy, who has always believed in me.

With special thanks to Susan Amerikaner and Amy Shields; Jack, Nancy, and Jeff Artenstein; Nita Bennett; Tom Doherty; Steve Farmer, M.S.W., and Nicole and Catherine Farmer; Drs. Susan and Peter Glaser; Gary Goldstein; Marika Gorissen and George Manning; Anne Goshen, M.S.W., and Dr. Warren Farrell; Nancy Granat, Anne Meyer and Jane Lorenz of Deerfield Citizens for Drug Awareness; Bob Horwich and Kathy Harshberger; Rene Leyva; Ellen, David, Jack, Joel, Marian, Michael, and Myra Moskowitz; Q. L. Pearce; Ray Raines, M.S.; Aaron, Dan, and Elly Wolf; and Sergeant Don Van Velzer and Officer Greg Boles of L.A.P.D.'s Project D.A.R.E.

Introduction

This book will help you to teach your child the most important lesson he or she will ever learn: to say "NO!" to drugs.

It's unfortunate, but these days teaching your child this lesson is not just a good idea—it's a necessity. Drug use has spread from the universities all the way down to the elementary schools. A recent national survey by the classroom publication *Weekly Reader* found that twenty-five percent of fourth graders say children their age feel "some" or "a lot" of pressure to try alcohol and other drugs. By the sixth grade, about one child in twenty is already actively experimenting.

If you look behind these startling statistics, you will find that *pressure* is a key factor. In most cases, it is pressure from peers that pushes children into their first experiences with drugs. This book will help you to teach your child how to say "NO" to this pressure.

But knowing how to say "NO" isn't enough. Your child has to *want* to say "NO." Your child has to understand that drug use is unhealthy and unwise, and that there are plenty of better alternatives. This book will help you to convey that message.

Parents often feel uncomfortable talking to their children about drugs. This book will help you feel more at ease by giving you background information, advice, and specific examples you can use. Read it once by yourself, and then go over the book with your child. There are illustrations and read-aloud stories for you and your child to look at, talk about, and think about together.

As you read this book, keep in mind that learning to say "NO!" to drugs is a skill that can last your child a long and healthy lifetime.

Chapter One

How Children Get Involved With Drugs

Most children who get involved with drugs come in contact with them a number of times before they start experimenting. The first drugs they use are typically cigarettes and alcohol, and they are usually invited to try them by friends, classmates, or older brothers and sisters. Most youngsters will resist for a while, but many give in when more pressure is applied.

In most cases, the experience isn't pleasant. Kids usually don't like the taste of alcohol at first, and cigarettes cause their eyes to water and make them cough. They're told they will like them better after a while, and those who try a few more times usually do.

In this first stage, children take these drugs only when it's convenient. They can take them or leave them alone, and there appear to be no bad consequences.

Some kids who try drugs never go beyond the experimental stage, but many graduate to occasional use. They no longer wait for others to offer them a drink or a smoke—they start to seek out drugs.

Drugs cost money, so many children get involved in the very inexpensive—and very damaging—practice of sniffing glue or white-out. Others take alcohol, pills, cough medicine, smokeless tobacco, cigarettes—or the money to buy them—from their parents. If they feel guilty, they may try to escape that feeling by increasing their drug use.

Drugs give them the illusion of well-being, the illusion of being far away from all problems. And they work every time. With continued use, kids grow more and more comfortable around drugs and may begin to use them more often. Youngsters normally develop a physical tolerance and find they need to take increasing amounts just to get the same effect. They have probably heard about other youngsters getting in trouble with drugs, but they almost never believe anything so bad could ever happen to them.

Little by little, many occasional users move on to regular use. They

1

COUGH
COUGH

often begin taking drugs to feel better whenever they're feeling down, whenever they're under stress—and even to heighten their enjoyment of already good times. Schoolwork generally slips, and friends not into drugs are often replaced by those who are. Denial is usually a big factor in drug abuse. Youngsters deny the negative impact drugs are having on their lives and minimize the amount they are using. Parents often see signs that something is wrong, but don't follow up.

It's not known what percentage of young children who start experimenting become addicted to alcohol and other drugs. (Among junior and senior high school students, the figure is known to be one in five.) But experts generally believe that the earlier children get involved with smoking, drinking, and other drug taking, the more likely they are to become heavy smokers, alcoholics, and abusers of other drugs.

Chapter Two

How to Teach Your Child to Say No to Drugs

The following four-part program will guide you in teaching your child about drugs and how to say "NO" to them. It will have a stronger, more lasting impact if, rather than going through it all at once, you space it over several days or weeks.

I. Teach Your Child About Drugs

The first step in teaching your child to say "NO" to drugs is to teach him or her a little about them. You needn't go into great detail. All your child really needs to know is:

1. "The only drugs that are good for you to take are those your mom or dad gives you when you're sick."

2. "Be especially careful to stay away from cigarettes and alcohol. Cigarette smoking makes your breath smell like an ashtray. It colors your teeth brown, and makes it hard for you to breathe. Alcohol makes it hard for you to think and play. It can cause you to do and say things that may embarrass you and other people. It can make you dizzy and cause you to get injured in accidents. Both cigarettes and alcohol make it hard for you to grow up strong and healthy."

You will note that the focus here, and throughout the book, is almost entirely on tobacco and alcohol. They are the "gateway drugs," meaning the great majority of kids who get involved with drugs try them first. It's only when kids get comfortable with them that they may start experimenting with marijuana (the "gateway" to the illegal

drugs), amphetamines, cocaine, PCP, LSD, ecstasy, and other drugs. So, if you succeed in teaching your child why and how to shun cigarettes and alcohol, the chances are very good that she or he will never get involved with any drugs.

Your child has probably heard that cigarettes and alcohol are bad, but the message could use some reinforcement from you, especially given the constant bombardment of ads saying the opposite. Besides, he or she may not know *why* they are bad. When you explain why, concentrate on the *short-term* negative effects. ("Smoking makes you smell bad." "Drinking alcohol makes you dizzy.") Cancer, cirrhosis of the liver, and other long-term negative effects are unlikely to be taken seriously by someone so young. Be sure to add somewhere in your discussion, "If anybody offers you any, even if it's a close friend or an adult, tell them 'NO!' and come tell me, okay?" Your reassurance that your child won't have to face the problem alone may make all the difference.

If you really want this lesson to have an impact on your child, make this a discussion, not a lecture. Children learn better and are more interested when they have a chance to participate. Here, for example, is a conversation I had with a kindergartner named Ellen:

ALAN: Ellen, you know there are some things that are good to put in your body and some things that are bad. Can you tell me some good things?

ELLEN: Orange juice.

ALAN: Great. What else?

ELLEN: Potatoes, milk, . . . medicine.

ALAN: Is *all* medicine good for you?

ELLEN: I don't know.

ALAN: Well, the answer's no. Just the medicine your mom or dad gives you when you're sick is good for you. Your brother's medicine is good for him, but not for you. Maybe it looks good and tastes good, but it might really hurt you. Same thing with a friend's medicine—or any drugs anybody else tries to give you.

ELLEN: Only my medicine is good for me.

ALAN: You got it! And only when you're sick and only when your mom or dad give it to you. Now, tell me some things that are bad to put into your body.

ELLEN (*smiling*): Dirt.

ALAN: Yuk! You're right about that! Eating dirt is bad for you. What else?

ELLEN: A friend's medicine.

ALAN: Very good! You remembered that from before. What else?

ELLEN (*shrugs her shoulders*): I don't know.

ALAN: Well, how about smoking cigarettes? Is that good for you?

ELLEN: No!

7

ALAN: Why not?

ELLEN: It's not healthy.

ALAN: How come?

ELLEN: It makes you cough and it makes your lungs black.

ALAN: Right. And it makes your breath and clothes and hair smell yucky. If anybody ever offers you a cigarette, you tell them "NO!" and tell your mom and dad, okay?

ELLEN: Okay.

ALAN: What else? What about alcohol? That's a drug too.

ELLEN: I know some kids who got drunk and got into a fight.

ALAN: Kids who drink often do a lot of stupid things. They say things they don't mean. They hurt other people and they hurt themselves in accidents. If anybody ever offers you a drink, tell them "No!" and run home and tell your mom or dad, okay?

ELLEN: Okay!

II. Weigh the Pros and Cons

Make two lists with your child, one labeled "Reasons for *Not* Taking Alcohol or Other Drugs" and the other "Reasons for Taking Alcohol and Other Drugs." Make it clear that by drugs, you mean anything except medicines that come from you or your spouse when your child is sick.

Let your child go first, thinking of as many reasons as she or he can, while one of you writes them down. Then, you add a few more, once again focusing on the *short-term* negative effects of drug taking.

Go over the list the two of you have made and remark that it only takes *one* good reason to say "NO"—and you've got *lots* of reasons.

This is what a sample list looks like:

REASONS FOR NOT TAKING ALCOHOL AND OTHER DRUGS:	REASONS FOR TAKING ALCOHOL AND OTHER DRUGS:
THEY MAKE YOU SICK. CIGARETTES MAKE YOU SMELL. THEY MAKE YOU COUGH. THEY MAKE YOUR LUNGS BLACK. BEER MAKES YOU DRUNK AND SILLY. IT MAKES YOU STUPID IN SCHOOL. YOU CAN'T DO YOUR HOMEWORK. YOU CAN GET INTO BIG TROUBLE. YOU CAN GET DIZZY AND HAVE AN ACCIDENT. CIGARETTES MAKE YOUR TEETH TURN BROWN	NONE!

Now that you've thought it out together, ask if it makes sense to try drugs. When your child says "NO," ask him or her to promise not to take drugs, no matter how much the peer pressure. Reassure your child that you'll always be available to support that decision.

This exercise is vital. It's been shown that children who clarify the issue and arrive at a definite decision *before* they are faced with the situation are more likely to say "NO!"

III. Teach Your Child to Say "NO!"

Tell your daughter or son that most kids start using alcohol and other drugs because they give in to pressure from friends and classmates. Even when friends and classmates aren't actively using coercion, your child may still feel pressure to fit in, to be "one of the gang." So, the best ways to avoid getting involved with drugs are:

1. *Stick with friends who don't use drugs.*
2. *Avoid places where kids who use drugs hang out.*

Some kids are introduced to drugs by babysitters, older relatives, or other adults. Young children inherently view anyone even a few years older as an authority figure and are likely to do as they say. So it's important that you teach your child that he or she must never take drugs from anyone except you and that anyone else who offers him or her a drug is breaking the law.

Point out that no matter how good or how careful she or he is, someday, someone may well offer her or him a drug. And that's why it's important to learn to say "NO!"

An assertive, definite "NO" is the best kind. That kind of no discourages further pressure. In an assertive "NO," your child
Stands up straight
Looks you in the eye
Speaks clearly and firmly.

Coach your child to say "NO" assertively. Here is how things went with Amy, a second grader:

ALAN (*writes "NO!" on a piece of paper*): Amy, what's this word?

AMY: No.

ALAN: Now, suppose I offered you a cigarette. How would you say no? . . . Hey, Amy, how about a smoke?

AMY (*says it quietly, looking down*): No.

ALAN: Oh, Amy. If you said it like that, I wouldn't believe you really meant it. Look at me and let me really hear you say it.

AMY (*giggling*): No!

ALAN: Pretty good, except for that giggle. That makes me think you're not serious. How about a real "NO!" Like this: "NO!"

AMY: NO! I don't want that cigarette!

ALAN: Terrific! You stood up straight, you looked me right in the eye, and you said it clearly. You really meant it that time!

AMY: NO! NO! NO!

There are five ways to say "NO." As you go over them, give your child a chance to practice each, paying attention both to what is said and how it's said.

1. Say "No thanks."

Want a beer?
No thanks.

2. Give a reason.

Say, how about some marijuana?
No thanks, smoke makes me cough.
It's not good for me.
My mom told me not to.
I'd get in trouble.

3. Say "NO!" over and over—as long as it takes. And if you get a lot of pressure, walk away.

Want some pot?
No thanks.
Come on, we'll get high!
No thanks.
Just a little!
No thanks.
Just this once. Come on!
No thanks. Bye.

12

4. Change the subject.

Let's drink some wine!
No thanks. You want to help me fly my kite?

5. Ignore the person.

Hey, want a cigarette?
———

Your child must learn to say "NO!" over and over again, for as long as it takes. And if he or she gets a lot of pressure, he or she should just walk away. Point out that some kids will often repeatedly ask others to try drugs, hoping to wear them down and win them over. But that won't happen to youngsters who know to say "NO, NO, NO!" for as long as it takes, and to walk away if necessary.

14

IV. Practice

Kids who have lots of practice saying "NO" find it easier to resist pressure to try drugs in real life. Pretend to be a peer of your child, and use these statements to elicit reactions and responses.

Hey, let's get high!

Want a sip of wine?

Here, try one of these pills. They taste like candy!

It's hot outside. My mom has some wine in the fridge. Want some?

The rest of us are going out back to smoke some cigarettes. How about you?

Here, have a cigarette. (*Pause for reply*)
If you don't, I won't be your friend. (*Pause*)
And I'll tell everybody you were chicken!

This party's boring. Let's go find somebody to buy us some beer.
You coming?

I just swiped some chewing tobacco from the drugstore. Want to try
some? (*Pause*) Just a little! C'mon!

Here, have a drink. (*Pause*)
But everybody's drinking! (*Pause*)
Come on! Don't be a party pooper. Drink! (*Pause*)
You're such a baby. Come on!

I know you have a big test today. Why not take one of these.
(*Pause*) Everybody's trying it!

16

Try some of this. (*Pause*)
It's just beer! (*Pause*)
You're a sissy!

Let's add some vodka to our orange juice and give it a real kick!

Don's folks are gone and everybody's partying over there. How about it? Here's your chance to try some booze!

Hey, want some pills? How much money have you got? (*Pause*) But you'll like it! (*Pause*) What are you, a baby?

My big sister got this medicine from the doctor. Let's try some!

There's nothing to do. Let's get wasted!

Say, I've got a can of beer. Want to split it?

This cherry cough syrup is great! Have some!

Chapter Three

How to Counter Pro-Drug Messages from the Media

Every day, unwanted guests come into your home: commercials promoting drugs and alcohol. Your child watches them on TV, hears them on the radio, and sees them in newspapers and magazines. It has been estimated that by the age of eighteen, the average child will have seen about 180,000 ads extolling the virtues of hundreds of brands of drugs and alcohol. Your child needs your help to understand these messages and view them critically.

Start by collecting some ads for cigarettes and alcohol and looking them over with your child. Point out that companies spend millions of dollars taking out these ads, trying to get you to buy what they sell. (This may be an obvious point to you, but may not be to your child.)

As you look over each ad, ask your youngster, "What do they want you to think?" Show how the ads subtly, and not so subtly, play on your weaknesses and tell us that smoking and drinking will help us:

to be strong and independent
to be attractive
to be grown-up
to be successful and wealthy
to be healthy
to be popular and loved

As you look over each ad, identify the benefit it promises and ask, "Is it true? Why or why not?" Give your child plenty of time to think it over.

I asked nine-year-old Michael, "What do you think? This man looks pretty strong, chopping wood like that. Will smoking make you strong?"

"No way!" he said. "Smoking makes you weak. You lose your breath and you cough all the time if you try to chop wood."

In working out your responses, it may help you to refer to this list:

What they want you to think

Strong and independent.

Attractive.

What really happens

Weak and addicted.

Unattractive. You'll have yellow and brown teeth, smelly breath, and smelly clothes.

19

Grown-up.	You're the same age you always were. Being grown-up really means thinking for yourself, not giving in to pressure, and learning to cope with your problems in a positive way.
Successful and wealthy.	Poorer. Drugs cost you a lot of money and don't make you any.
Healthy.	Unhealthy. Cigarettes make you short of breath, coat your lungs with tar, and make you cough a lot. Alcohol can give you hangovers, make you throw up, hurt your mind, your heart, and your liver.
Popular and loved.	Unpopular with non-users. And even among users, lots of people act in ways that cost them friends when they drink. Your parents and your *real* friends will like and love you without your using drugs.

Some ads have the added message, "Everybody's doing it!" It's important to counter this, as many youngsters believe that everyone in junior high and beyond is taking drugs and alcohol. They tend to see it as the grown-up (and thus, attractive) thing to do. You can set the record straight by making the point that, in fact, most kids are not involved with drugs. And even among adults, two-thirds don't smoke and, while most do drink, many do it only on special occasions and many regret ever having gotten started.

Pay special attention to beer ads. They commonly convey the "Everybody's doing it!" message as well as "Drinking beer is a great way to spend time with friends!" and "It's a terrific reward after a hard day's work!" Point out that beer has succeeded in achieving the image of a friendly, harmless drink, thanks to millions of dollars of advertising. But the truth is that beer's active ingredient, ethyl alcohol, is the same drug that's the active ingredient in hard liquor. In fact, a

can of beer, whether light or regular, has just as much ethyl alcohol as a shot of whiskey.

Ask your child, "What do the companies that paid money for these ads want you to do?" The answer will always be: "Give us your money. Buy our cigarettes. Buy our alcohol."

Ask your child, "What's the bad side they don't show?"

"Jonathan," I asked one eight-year-old, "all the drinkers at this party look so happy. Is there a bad side to drinking they aren't showing you?"

"Yes," he answered.

"Tell me one bad thing that might happen to these people."

"They might get drunk and act stupid," he said.

"Like hit somebody or say something they didn't mean?"

"Yeah. Or get in a car crash. Or they might throw up, or get dizzy and fall down."

21

"That's right. The ads try to fool you, just like kids who try to get you to use drugs try to fool you. They never tell you the bad side."

Point out that "drugs are fun" is also a common theme in records, videos, movies, and TV shows. Producers and big companies use that theme to seem "in," to entertain, and ultimately to sell records, videos, and tickets, and to get people to watch their shows. But they don't show the bad side. Point out that often the rock stars who perform in these pro-drug records and videos and the actors who appear in these pro-drug movies and TV shows are in the news for getting in trouble with drugs. Athletes, actors, rock stars, and kids—all human beings can get badly hurt by drugs.

One thing more: Don't make this just a one-time discussion. The media doesn't.

Chapter Four

How to Build an Anti-Drug Climate in Your Home

Teaching your child about drugs, how to say "NO," and how to resist pro-drug media messages is vital. To really "drug-proof" your child, consider taking the following additional steps at home.

Share More of Your Time and Yourself

Youngsters whose parents set aside time to communicate with them and who are warm and affectionate toward them are less likely to use drugs, according to a research study led by Dr. Judith Brook of Mt. Sinai School of Medicine in New York. The opposite is also true, especially for fathers: adolescent drug users tend to have fathers who spend little time with them, fight with them, and have difficulty showing affection.

The implications are obvious: Many of us need to make a point of sharing more of our time and ourselves with our children. Consider setting aside a special quiet time to spend with your child each day. During this time, discuss topics of interest to your child and look for opportunities to be affectionate, to praise and encourage your child.

Discuss Feelings with Your Child

When you speak with your child, make a special effort to discuss her or his feelings about daily events and problems. Resist the urge to label those feelings as "good" or "bad," or to say your child should or shouldn't feel a certain way. Children need to know it's O.K. to have and to express feelings like anger, fear, frustration, and love.

Children who bottle up their feelings often seek release through alcohol and other drugs.

Children learn by example, so perhaps the best way to encourage your child to open up is to talk about some of your own feelings. This may also be important as it will provide your child with a more balanced view of life. Many kids, constantly exposed to commercials promising quick relief from all life's ills by taking one drug or another, grow up thinking they're never supposed to feel pain, that it's not acceptable to feel uncomfortable or depressed. That kind of attitude, many experts believe, predisposes kids to drug taking. Hearing about some of your disappointments and conflicts and the ways you are trying to work them out will provide both a more accurate picture of the way life really is and an example for your child to follow.

Promote Better Alternatives

As part of your program to prevent your child from getting involved with alcohol and other drugs, it's important for you to promote positive alternatives. TV watching isn't enough—you need to encourage your child to pursue active recreational activities, hobbies, and interests with other children. A youngster who's busy will seldom have much interest in drugs. A youngster who has several sets of friends will be more resistant to peer pressure. Give your child some meaningful work to do, like caring for younger siblings or helping out elderly relatives. Drug abuse is often born of aimlessness, and a child who feels important probably won't find drugs very attractive.

Be Involved in Parents Groups and School Affairs

Join PRIDE or the National Federation of Parents for Drug-Free Youth, the leading anti-drug parent organizations in the United States. Their addresses and toll-free numbers are listed in the back of this book.

Join your local PTA and be actively involved in your child's education. Be sure your school has an anti-drug program and if it doesn't, urge school authorities to start one. Even when your child gets into junior and senior high school, stay involved and have periodic conferences with your child's teachers. Your involvement will encourage

your child to get a good education and may someday alert you to one of the early signs of drug use: lack of interest in school.

Be a Positive Role Model

Children imitate the adults around them, and what we *do* sends a far more powerful message than what we say. For example, studies have found that over eighty percent of parents who drink have youngsters who drink, while seventy percent of parents who don't drink have youngsters who abstain. So it's important that we set a good example for our children when it comes to alcohol and other drugs.

If you smoke, consider quitting, as about ten percent of smokers did last year alone. And if you choose not to, discuss the subject with your child, as a construction worker named Tom did one day:

"Richie," Tom said, "you know I'm a two-pack-a-day man, and I've tried to quit, but I just haven't been able to. Now I'm worried that someday you'll take it up and you'll think it's O.K. because your old man is doing it. I want to set you straight—it's not. I wish I'd never started. It's not good for you. It makes me cough when I'm out there working, and sometimes when I'm just sitting here in my favorite chair. It makes my clothes smell, and might kill me while I'm still young. It was a mistake for me to get started and I don't want you to make the same mistake.''

If you drink alcohol, consider drinking only when your child is not around or, as a start, drinking in moderation. If your family typically drinks wine with meals or as part of religious rituals, there is a risk that your child will come to enjoy the mood swing and seek it out more often. Grape juice, as many families, churches, and synagogues are finding, makes a fine, safe substitute.

Chapter Five

How to Deal with Some Typical Problems

If your child reports having been offered alcohol or other drugs and having turned them down, be sure to praise her or him both for saying "NO" and for telling you. If the offer took place in school, contact the child's teacher and the principal. If it took place in the community and involved tobacco, it's usually best to work things out with the other child's parents. If it involved alcohol or any other drug, both the parents and the police should be contacted. Don't think you're being overly protective. Drug abuse is a big problem that usually starts small, and you've sometimes got to take serious measures to defend your child.

Despite your best efforts, your child may still get involved with drugs, so it's important that you recognize the signs. If you find alcohol, drugs, or drug-related items in your child's possession, it's *very* likely that she or he is using drugs. If you answer yes to any of the following questions, your child *may* be in trouble:

Has your child suddenly lost interest in formerly enjoyable activities?

Has your child begun missing school a lot? Are your child's grades falling?

Are you suddenly having discipline problems with your child?

Has your child suddenly changed friends? Does your child avoid bringing these friends home?

Is your child withdrawing from the family? Spending more time away from home or more time alone in his or her room?

Has your child become dirtier? Sloppier?

Has your child started coming home late?

Is your child borrowing money? Stealing?

Do your child's clothes or body smell of tobacco?

Are your child's eyes red, dilated, or contracted? Does your child have a constant runny nose?

A "yes" to any one of these questions may simply be indicative of normal growing pains. Be especially concerned, however, if you answered "yes" to more than one question. Explain to your child why you are worried and ask your child directly if he or she is using alcohol or other drugs. If you get a "yes," ask where the child got the drugs and from whom. Follow the guidelines at the start of this chapter in notifying your child's teacher, the principal, the other child's parents, or the police.

Even if you get a "no," don't stop there. Spend time with your child talking over these problems, voice your concern about drug abuse, and get to know your child's friends and their parents.

If your child admits taking drugs or if it seems your child is involved, you should make it clear that you consider drug taking foolish and unacceptable and that you will not allow it. If the problem persists, contact your school psychologist or other professionals qualified to deal with substance abuse.

Many parents ignore these warning signals, hoping that the problem will go away or that the child will outgrow it. They may even lie for the child, withhold information from spouses, and make excuses to people who accuse the child. But drug abuse is a problem that typically only gets worse, so the sooner it's faced, the better.

Chapter Six

The following stories will help your child to learn more about the dangers of drugs and will provide a fuller understanding of exactly how to say "NO" to them. I suggest you read these stories in a relaxed atmosphere and that you take your time. Don't try to go through them all in one sitting. Let your child be your guide, and continue reading only so long as he or she appears interested.

The children in these stories always do the right thing. Your child should ideally answer the question, "What would *you* do?" in each story with a similar response. Be especially certain to stress the importance not only of saying "NO," but also of telling you of any offers of drugs.

Reading these stories with your child and discussing the situations and the proper reaction will reinforce your child's ability to resist pressure when faced with similar real-life situations.

TRAVIS'S STORY

Trina and Travis were playing hide-and-go-seek. Trina ran behind a bush to hide—and stepped on a bottle full of pills!

"Should we try one?" asked Trina.

"No!" Travis said. "That's dumb!
Those pills could hurt us."

Travis carefully picked up all the pills,
so no one could get hurt. Then he ran
home and gave them to his mom.
 What would you do?

DORIS'S STORY

Doris was at a wedding party where almost everyone, including the kids, was drinking champagne and dancing. A waiter came by and poured her a drink. Her parents were off dancing and no one would notice if she drank it. And she was curious.

But Doris's dad had once lost his job because of drinking. He told her that one in ten adults and one in five kids who

start drinking end up getting in trouble
because of it. So Doris decided it just
wasn't worth the chance.

Doris turned to the boy at the next table. "Hey, you want to dance?" she said. The boy gave her a big smile. Doris felt terrific as they danced up a storm!

What would you do?

AARON'S STORY

George was always getting into trouble. He drank alcohol, smoked cigarettes, cheated on tests, and cut classes. One day while Aaron was walking home, George came by on his bike and asked Aaron if he wanted a ride. Aaron knew it wasn't smart to make friends with boys who use drugs.

"No thanks," Aaron said. "I like
walking."

"Suit yourself," George said. And he
pedaled away.
    What would you do?

MYRA'S STORY

Myra went to the clubhouse after school and found two of her best friends in there, smoking. They offered her a cigarette.

Myra liked the girls a lot, and she was afraid of what might happen if she said no:

Would they still want to be friends?

Would they call her a chicken?
Would they call her a baby?
"NO!" she said anyway. "My mom told
me it's not healthy."

"I don't really like it either," said one of the girls. "Let's all go roller skating!"
And so they did.
What would you say?

TOM'S STORY

Tom came home and found his big
brother Roger and a bunch of Roger's
friends drinking beer.

"Here," Roger said to Tom with a
smile. "Have a sip." He held out a can
of beer.

"No thanks," Tom said.

"Just a sip! Don't be a baby!" Roger said.

Tom knew that saying "NO" to things that are bad for you isn't being a baby.

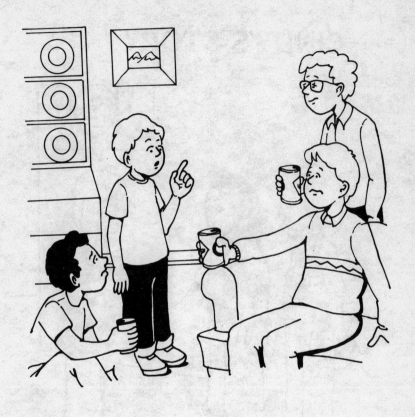

Tom looked Roger straight in the eye.
"I said, 'No thanks!' I'm going out
to play." That night, he told his parents
what had happened and they talked
to Roger.
What would you say?

CINDY'S STORY

Cindy was new at school. One day,
two girls in her class came up and said,
"You can be our friend if you try this."

Cindy knew that the only safe drugs
were those her mom and dad gave her.
Besides, who needs friends who'd only
like you if you took drugs?

Cindy said, "No thanks!" and she ran
home and told her father.

What would you do?

JEFF'S STORY

Jeff and a friend were playing one day when his friend said, "Here, try this." It was a cigarette.

Jeff knew that cigarettes aren't healthy: they make your hair and your breath smell yucky. They stain your teeth brown. They coat your insides with tar.

"No thanks!" he said.
"Come on! It'll be our secret," said his
friend.

"NO!" Jeff said. "My mom told me never to make secrets about drugs." And then he walked home and told his mom.

What would you say?

AMY'S STORY

   Amy's parents went out one evening
and left her with a sitter named Cynthia.
   Amy and Cynthia watched TV and ate
popcorn. Cynthia kept going to the
kitchen and the bathroom. Amy thought
she was drinking, because her breath
smelled funny. Before long, Cynthia
could hardly walk or talk straight.
   "Come on," Cynthia said. "Let's go to
the 7-Eleven and get some more popcorn."
Then she hiccuped!

Amy knew she must never, never
drive anywhere with anyone who was
drunk.

"NO!" said Amy. She went into her
bedroom and stayed there until bedtime,
and in the morning she told her parents
what happened.
What would you do?

JUAN'S STORY

Juan liked Doug, but became worried when he heard that Doug sold marijuana to several kids at school. One day while they were in Doug's room, Doug told Juan he had a surprise.

"What is it?" Juan asked excitedly. "A new book?"

"No," said Doug. "Guess again."

"Baseball cards?" Juan asked.

"No!" said Doug. "I've got some pot! Want some?"

"No thanks," Juan said, looking him squarely in the eye.

"But it's free!" Doug said.

"No thanks," Juan said. Juan was disappointed. Doug had just been pretending to be his friend all along. All he had really wanted was to get him started on marijuana and make him a customer!

"No thanks," Juan repeated, as confident as ever. "I've got to go home now." And he went home and told the whole story to his father.

What would you do?

DONNA'S STORY

Donna was new at school. She made
a big mistake and made friends with a
bunch of kids who used drugs.

"Come on!" they said to her and
offered her some drugs. "Don't be
chicken!"

Donna said, "NO!"

"Just this once!" they demanded.

"NO!" she said again. Donna's big brother had warned her never to use drugs, not even once. He said, "It happened to me. 'Just one time' led to 'just one more time.' The only safe way is to never get started."

Donna looked her "friends" in the eye.
"NO!" she said firmly and ran home and
told her parents.

Donna decided she needed to find
some new friends who didn't use drugs.
For a few days she was lonely, but then
she met Beth, and soon she had a whole
group of friends who never used drugs.

What would you do?

SAM'S STORY

Sam was at a friend's party when someone passed around a pack of cigarettes. Lots of kids took one, but Sam said, "No thanks. Smoking makes me cough."

Later, two of the kids at the party said
they admired Sam for speaking up.
What would you do?

JENNY'S STORY

Jenny was walking to class and passed a girl sitting on a bench.

"Hey, want to get high?" the girl asked.

Jenny knew the smartest way to handle trouble is to avoid it in the first place. So she didn't say anything. She just kept walking, and when she got to class she told her teacher what had happened.

What would you do?

PETER'S STORY

One day, Peter came home and found his older brother Josh and a bunch of Josh's friends hanging around and chewing tobacco.

One of Josh's friends spit his tobacco into a bowl. Yuck, Peter thought, it looks terrible!

"Want to try some?" the boy asked,
smiling. Peter noticed that his teeth were
stained brown.

Not if my teeth are going to look ugly like yours, Peter thought. But he said, "No thanks, I've got to go brush my teeth and do some homework."
What would you say?

KRIS'S STORY

Kris had just moved to a new neighborhood. She was lonely until she met a bunch of girls from down the block. They invited her to a slumber party. She was glad—until she saw that everybody was smoking.

"Come on, Kris, join us!" one girl said.

Kris knew that smoking isn't smart. Her dad smoked, and he smelled like smoke and was always short of breath. He often said he wished he'd never started.

"No thanks," Kris said. "My dad told me not to."

"Hey, it's a party!" another girl said. "Loosen up!"

"No thanks," Kris said again, but the pressure was getting pretty heavy. Kris called home and asked her mom to come pick her up. And on the way home, Kris told her mom what had happened.

What would you do?

BRIAN'S STORY

One day Brian was out walking by the river when he saw Jerry and Jim, two of his friends from school. They were sitting on the riverbank drinking beer.

"Have a beer!" said Jerry. His words were a little slurred.

"No thanks," said Brian.

"Just a little!" said Jerry.

"No thanks," Brian said confidently. He knew that he could just say "NO" over and over and nobody could ever force him to drink anything.

"Come on!" said Jim. "It won't kill you!"

Brian looked Jim and Jerry right in the eye. "No thanks," he said again. He felt terrific saying "NO" like that! Then he walked home and told his mom.

What would you say?

ISABEL'S STORY

Isabel noticed that her best friend Dorothy was looking sick. Dorothy said she was just getting over a cold and had some pills to take to get well. "Want to try one?" Dorothy said.

74

Isabel knew that the only medicines that were safe for her to take were the ones she got from her parents.

"No thanks," Isabel said. That night,
she told her mom what had happened.
What would you say?

RALPH'S STORY

Ralph was at a friend's house after school. The friend said, "There's nothing to do. Let's get high!"

Ralph knew there were a million and one better things to do than taking drugs. They could read, watch TV, play catch, go bike riding, paint, draw, fly kites, visit another friend, play checkers, climb a tree, play handball . . .

"No," Ralph said. "Let's play
basketball instead!"
What would you say?

ELLEN MICHELE'S STORY

Usually, Bob hardly noticed Ellen Michele. But at a party he came over, started talking with her, and offered to share a marijuana cigarette.

Ellen Michele really wanted Bob to like her, so she didn't say "NO," exactly. Instead, she said, "No thanks. I don't want to give you my cold."

At the park a week later, Bob offered
her another joint. Ellen Michele still
wanted to be friends, but not if she had

to keep making excuses or take up
smoking.

"No thanks," she said. "I've decided
not to take drugs."

What would you say?

DAVID'S STORY

David is smart. He never drinks
alcohol or uses drugs.

One day, a girl he liked came up to
him after class. "David," she said. "I
know you don't use drugs, but there's a
big pot party Friday night and I want you
to go with me."

David knew the best way to never get
in trouble with drugs is to stay away
from the people who use them and the
places where they hang out.

"No thanks," David said. "I've got to
babysit my little sister."
What would you say?

STACEY'S STORY

Stacey was playing handball after school when some friends said, "Hey, let's go get some beer!"

"NO!" said Stacey. "My mom told me it's not good for me!"

"Oh, grow up!" said one friend, sounding like she couldn't believe what she had heard. But Stacey knew better.

Stacey knew growing up means deciding
things for yourself, and not because
somebody tries to force you.

"NO," Stacey said calmly.

"If Stacey won't, I won't either,"
Stacey's friend Arlene said. They had a
great time playing while the others went
off and got drunk. Later, Stacey told her
mother what had happened.

What would you do?

RAY'S STORY

Ray was practicing pitching and
Shawn was practicing catching.
"Strike one!" said Shawn.
"Strike two!"
"Strike three!"
"Strike four!"
Ray laughed at Shawn's joke, but he'd
been watching his friend Joel, who was
sitting in the stands.

Joel was talking with some boys from
school, some boys who used drugs. Ray
knew that if Joel got involved with those
boys, he'd probably get involved with
drugs, too.

"Joel," Ray called out, "come down here and try to hit while I pitch. It's no fun practicing without a batter!"

What would you do?

ASAKO'S STORY

Asako and her friend Kitt were sitting together after school when a friend of Kitt's asked them if they wanted some marijuana.

"NO!" said Asako right away.
"Oh, grow up!" said Kitt's friend.
"Yeah, don't be chicken," said Kitt.

"No, I'm smart!" said Asako.
"Marijuana isn't good for me." Asako
walked home and told her parents what
had happened.

What would you do?

MICHAEL'S STORY

Michael was walking home when a
man came up to him and asked him if
he wanted some drugs. The man
reached into his pocket and took out
some red and white pills.

Michael knew that the only drugs that were safe for him to take were the medicines his mother gave him when he was sick.

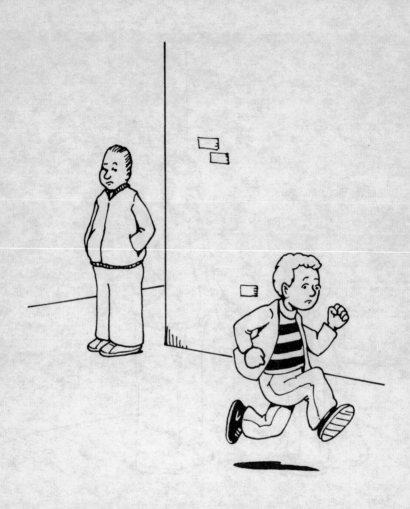

Michael was so afraid that the word "NO!" stuck in his throat. He backed away and then ran all the way home, where he told everybody what had happened.

What would you do?

LINDA'S STORY

Linda was sad. Somebody had stolen her new bike from school. Linda looked everywhere at school, but couldn't find it. Her mom drove her all over the neighborhood, but it was gone.

That night, Linda's parents went out, and Linda and her older brother Zack were at home alone.

"Here, have some of this wine," Zack said.

Linda knew that drinking wouldn't solve her problem. It wouldn't bring her

bike back. And if she got started, it might give her a much worse problem: drinking!

"No thanks," she said. "I've got to study." When her parents came home, Linda told them what had happened, and they talked to Zack about using alcohol.

What would you say?

CRAIG'S STORY

Craig was worried about his big
spelling test.

"Here, have some pot!" said Mark.

"No thanks," Craig answered. "I need a clear mind to study, not a mind full of drugs."

Then Craig went home and told his mom and dad.

What would you do?

BEE'S STORY

Howard invited Bee to a party
Saturday night. Friday, in class, she
heard one of the girls say, "The party at

Howard's is going to be terrific—lots of
wine and no parents!"

Bee knew the best way to avoid
trouble is to stay away.
    She went to a movie with a friend
instead.
    What would you do?

JACK'S STORY

Jack was resting on a park bench. He had just played a hard game of handball and was tired.

A man sat down near him and started eating some candy. After a while he offered Jack some.

Jack loved candy, but his parents had
taught him never to take any from
strangers. "Sometimes the candy they
give you can hurt you," they had said.

"No thanks!" Jack said, and he went
back to his game.
   What would you say?

NANCY'S STORY

Nancy went to a party and found that
lots of kids were smoking and drinking
beer. They kept offering her some.

Nancy felt a little uncomfortable and
scared. Her parents had told her she

never had to ask anyone's permission to
use the phone when she felt uncomfortable or scared.

Nancy called her parents and asked
her dad to come right away and take her
home.

What would you do?

ELLIOT'S STORY

Elliot got in trouble with his mom and dad and wasn't allowed to watch TV for a whole week.

His friend Eric came to visit and said, "Let's smoke a joint!"

Elliot knew that marijuana wasn't good for him and could get him in really big trouble.

"No thanks," Elliot said. "Let's just ride our bikes."

"It's only a joint!" Eric said, not giving up.

"*No thanks!*" Elliot said, pedaling
away. "You coming?" he called back.
   Eric rode after him. Later, Elliot told
his parents what had happened.
   What would you do?

SUSAN'S STORY

Susan went to the park with friends
who didn't use drugs. They played
kickball and tetherball and handball.

They had a lot of fun and laughed a lot.
When the ice-cream man came around,
they got some snow cones.

What happened next? Nothing bad!
Choose friends who don't use drugs and
you won't have to say "NO!"

If you are interested in joining the national network of parents who are working to prevent drug abuse, contact the following organizations:

National Federation of Parents for Drug-Free Youth
8730 Georgia Avenue, Suite 200
Silver Spring, MD 20910
1–800–554–KIDS

PRIDE: Parents' Resource Institute for Drug Education
100 Edgewood Avenue, Suite 1216
Atlanta, GA 30303
1–800–241–7946